CONTENTS

CHARACTERS

James

James likes to be in charge. He's the eldest and always thinks that he knows best, but his friends don't always agree!

Alex

Alex isn't impressed with the way James bosses everyone around. He has good ideas too ... if only James would listen.

Scarlett

Scarlett is caring and practical. She is good at looking after her friends.

BURIED ALIVE!

Richard Cooper

SERIES CONSULTANT: LORRAINE PETERSEN

RISING STARS

NASEN House, 4/5 Amber Business Village, Amber Close, Amington,
Tamworth, Staffordshire B77 4RP

Rising Stars UK Ltd.
22 Grafton Street, London W1S 4EX
www.risingstars-uk.com

Published 2009

Cover design: Burville-Riley Partnership
Illustrator: Neil Smith
Text design and typesetting: Andy Wilson for Green Desert Ltd.
Publisher: Gill Budgell
Editor: Catherine Gilhooly
Series consultant: Lorraine Petersen

British Library Cataloguing in Publication Data.
A CIP record for this book is available from the British Library

ISBN   978-1-84680-503-5

Printed by Craft Print International Limited, Singapore

Characters

Leo

Leo is a good friend and he can be
brave when he needs to be.

Fin

Fin is friends with everyone.
He can be very brave too,
but he's really scared
of water.

Narrator

The narrator tells the story.

Scene 1

THE NIGHTMARE BEGINS

Narrator   Five friends are on an activity weekend
in Wales. They are exploring caves
deep underground with an
adult leader called Dave.
Suddenly, there is a rock fall.

James   Quick! Leo, Fin come here.
Dave is hurt.

Narrator   Dave has been knocked out and he is
bleeding quite badly.

Scarlett   He's still breathing.
We need to get him to a doctor.

Leo   I've got my mobile. I'll call for help.

Narrator   Leo dials 999 but he can't get a signal.

Alex   Maybe we could carry him out ...
or go for help?

Fin   OH NO!

Narrator   The others turn to see what
Fin is shouting about. There has been
another rock fall. The tunnel
is blocked!

Leo   What are we going to do?
I don't like the dark.
I'm scared.

Scarlett We all have our helmet lamps.
How long do the batteries last?

Fin About three hours. We've been
down here for an hour already.

Alex We are going to have to get out
of this mess ourselves. We need
to find another way out.

James Who asked you, short-stuff?
I'm the oldest so that makes me
the new leader. Do you all agree?

Alex Okay James, what do you suggest
we do?

James Right, we need to gather all the things
which are going to be useful.
Who still has food and water?

Scarlett I have a snack bar and my water bottle.

Fin Me too.

Alex I've got a bag of sweets I brought
with me too. We can share those.

Leo   I ate all my food on the bus trip here!

Scarlett   We'll need to share out the supplies so nobody goes hungry.

James   Good idea, Scarlett. Now let's get moving. We have to find a way out before the lamps go out. If we're left in the dark, we may never get out alive!

Narrator They stop Dave's bleeding by tying a scarf around the cut. Then they set off down a tunnel. The path is rocky and uneven. They stumble on for half an hour.

Leo   This is getting us nowhere.
               We'll never find a way out.

James   We've got to keep going,
               before our battery lamps go out.
               Now get a move on!

Scarlett   Poor Dave, I hope he's going to be okay.

Fin   Dave will be stuck here forever – like us
               – unless we get out soon.

Alex   I think we should take this turning on
               the left – I just felt a slight breeze.

James   Rubbish! Now keep going.
               Come on, move it.

Alex   But ...

Scarlett   Wait, I think I felt something too.

Fin   I can hear something!
It sounds like water.

Leo   Come on, we need to take a look.

Narrator   James leads the team towards the sound of the water. They arrive in a large cave with a stream flowing through it.

James   Look, a stream! The water must flow to the outside world somehow. We can follow it. See, I told you I was a good leader!

Alex   Okay James, but we still haven't found a way out.

Scarlett   Look, the stream runs through that tunnel. Perhaps that could be a way out.

Fin   I can't swim. I hope it's not deep.

Scene 1   The nightmare begins

Leo   You can hold on to me, Fin.

Narrator The team enter the water very
              carefully. It is waist deep. They start to
              wade through the tunnel one at a time.
              Fin is holding on to Leo very tightly.

James   Oh, this water is freezing!
              Keep moving, guys, or we'll freeze
              to death!

Alex   The floor is slippery. Be careful!

Scarlett Are you okay back there? Leo? Fin?

Leo   Fin, you're holding my neck
              too tightly.

Fin   Don't let go of me, Leo. I'm scared!

Narrator Suddenly at the front of the line,
              James slips and is washed downstream
              by the force of the water.

James   Argh! Help …

Alex   James! Oh no! Come on everyone, we've got to follow him.

Scarlett   Okay, let's go with the flow of the water.

Leo   Hold on, Fin. We'll go together. Ready?

Fin   Ready as I'll ever be.
I'm not letting go!

Narrator The team are carried along by the water. It is fast and they are swept through the tunnel. There is lots of coughing, spluttering and splashing. At last, they arrive in a large pool and climb out.

Scene 1   The nightmare begins

James   There you are! What kept you?

Alex   I think we're all okay.

Scarlett   I'm freezing cold and hungry.
Who's got the pack of supplies?

Fin   Leo had it. He was in charge of the food.

Leo   Err, I'm sorry but the food is gone.
I couldn't hold on to Fin and the pack
at the same time.

Narrator   Cold, wet and hungry, the team sit
and rest. After a few minutes, the only
thing they can do is get up, move on
and hope for the best.

Buried Alive!

Scene 2

A LONG WAY DOWN

James   Okay, let's try this way.
There's another tunnel over here.

Fin   Why should we listen to you, James?
Your 'follow the stream' idea has left us
soaking wet and freezing cold!

Leo   Yeah, and starving. Still, that's the only
way out, I suppose.

Scarlett   My lamp just flickered.
I think the battery
is running down.

Alex   The batteries are running down
             on all the lamps. Come on,
             we haven't got any time to lose.

Narrator The team stumble on until they come
             to a big hole in the ground.
             The path continues on the other side
             but they need to find a way across.

James   Whoa! Stop, everyone. There's a
             massive hole in the ground!
             We need to get across.

Fin   How deep is it?

Leo   My light can't shine that far to see.

Alex   I'll drop this stone down. Let's see how
             long it takes to hit something.

Scarlett Okay, quiet, everyone. Let's listen.

Narrator Alex picks up a small rock and drops it
             down the hole. The team hear nothing
             for a few seconds, then a distant splash.

James   That took ages. This is one deep hole.

Leo   I didn't need to know that.

Fin   We can't go back, we have to get across.

Scarlett   Right, I'm going to jump first. Stand back everyone.

Alex   Wait! She needs to see properly. Everyone shine their lamps on the edges of the hole.

Narrator   Everyone lights the way and Scarlett takes a run-up. She leaps and lands safely on the other side.

James   Huh, if a girl can do it, anyone can.
Leo, you go next.

Leo   No, I need to build myself up to jump. Fin, you go next.

Fin   Okay, here goes!

Alex   Great leap, Fin! That would have broken the school long jump record!

Scarlett   Right, come on then James, your turn.

Narrator   James makes the leap, and then Alex. The only one left to jump is Leo.

Leo   I can't run that fast. I won't get enough speed up.

James   Come on, Leo. Everyone shine their lamps so he can see.

Fin   Come on, Leo. Take a big run-up.

Alex   Here he comes, make room for him
              to land.

Scarlett Wait, my lamp ... no!

Narrator Just as Leo starts his run-up,
              Scarlett's lamp goes out!
              Leo jumps but doesn't make it.
              He is clinging on to a ledge about
              two metres down in the hole.

Leo   Argh! Help me! I think I've broken
              my ankle.

James   That was close. I thought we'd lost him.

Alex   He's hurt. We have to get him back up.

Scarlett Leo, can you climb back up?

Narrator Leo tries to stand on the ledge
              but his ankle *is* broken.
              He can just about kneel upright.

Leo   I can't stand up. I think my ankle
         really is broken.

James   Oh, this is all we need right now!

Fin   Look, we need to get him out of the hole.
         Think of something!

Scarlett We haven't got any rope.
         What can we do?

Alex   I know, let's use our clothes!

Narrator Alex and Fin take off their wet jumpers
         and tie them together. They lower
         their 'rope' down to Leo.

Leo   It's not long enough, I can't reach it!

Fin   James and Scarlett, we'll have to use
         your jumpers as well.

Scarlett Okay, it will make it stronger too.

James   Let me tie the knots, I was in the Scouts
         until last year.

Alex   Here Leo, tie this round you. We'll pull you up!

Narrator The rope made of jumpers is lowered to Leo again.
             This time he ties it round himself.

Fin   Okay, pull everyone!

Scarlett Phew, he's heavy.

James   All those pies mate, all those pies ...

Alex   Heave! He's nearly up!

Leo   Quickly guys, I can feel the knots coming loose! Argh!

HELLO! HELLO!

Narrator	As Leo reaches the top, the jumpers come loose and he starts to fall. Just in the nick of time, Alex grabs his hand. Leo lands in a heap on the floor.

Fin   That was close. Who tied the knots?

Alex   James said he was in the Scouts.

James   Well, I was until they kicked me out!

Scarlett Never mind, the important thing is Leo is safe.

Leo   Safe for the moment. We still need to get to the surface and now I can't walk.

Scene 3

INTO THE DARK

Narrator	The team struggle on. Leo is helped by Fin and Scarlett. Only four lamps are still working.
James	Okay, let's get moving. I'll go first.
Alex	I'll go at the back so you can all be in my light.
Fin	Leo, I'll take one arm. Scarlett, you take the other.
Leo	I can just about hop on one foot but ... ouch!

Scarlett   Sorry Leo, I slipped. It will be slow
but we've got to carry on.

Narrator   The team work their way slowly
along the rocky tunnel.

James   Careful here, guys.
There's lots of sharp rocks.

Alex   Try and keep closer together.

Fin   It's really difficult to see.

Leo   Oh no! My lamp is out now!

Scarlett   We've only got three lamps left.
There can't be much battery time to go!

Narrator   The team starts to feel very worried.
If all the lamps go out they will be in
total darkness.

Alex   My lamp should have more life.
I switched it off earlier to save power.

James   Well, good for you! Now, why ...

Fin   Argh! My arm, I've bashed it
on a rock!

Leo   Don't drop me. Ouch!

Scarlett   There's blood everywhere.
Stop, everyone.

Narrator   The team stop. Scarlett bandages
Fin's arm with a ripped up T-shirt.

Fin   I can walk, but I can't lift Leo.

Scarlett   I can't carry him on my own,
he's too heavy.

Alex   Me neither.
Who's the strongest?

James   I am!

Alex Are you sure?

James Of course I'm sure.
Why are you getting at me?

Alex It's just that you've been really bossy
since we left Dave behind. You haven't
listened to us and ... well, you've made
some mistakes.

James Like what?

Fin Like getting us all soaked
in the stream ...

Scarlett And not making the knots
on the jumper rope tight enough.

Narrator There is a long pause. James looks at
each of his friends in turn. He thinks
about what they have said.

James I suppose you might have a point.
I'm sorry I didn't listen, but I'll make
up for it.
I'll start by giving Leo a piggyback.

30

Leo Thank you, James. I don't want to be left alone in the dark.

James Nobody's being left behind, Leo. We're all in this together, right team?

Alex, **Fin**, **Scarlett**, **Leo** (*together*)
Right!

Narrator The team move slowly on. Alex is at the front, James is carrying Leo, and Fin and Scarlett are at the back.

Fin We seem to be going upwards.

Alex Perhaps we're getting close to the surface!

James Maybe, but the path has been going up and down for ages.

Leo Hold on, what's that beeping noise?

Scarlett It sounds like a mobile phone!

Narrator Leo's mobile has picked up a signal!

Fin   I thought it would have been ruined by the water.

Leo   It was in my waterproof bum-bag!

Scarlett   I shouldn't have laughed at you for wearing it here!

James   Brilliant, now let me dial 999.

Narrator   James gets through and speaks to an operator.

James   Hello? Hello? Can you hear me? We're trapped in Bone Cave near Brecon. We ...

Leo   The signal is weak. They can't hear him!

Scarlett   Shush! Let him speak.

Fin   Oh no, my lamp's just gone out!

Narrator James can hear the operator
              but they can't hear him.
              Suddenly the phone goes dead.

James   No! The phone battery is dead,
              just like three of our lamps.

Alex   Well, at least they will have logged
              the call.

Leo   Yes, they'll know we're down here ...
              and they'll send a rescue team for us
              and for Dave.

Fin   Maybe there is a rescue team
              on the way already!

Alex   You're right Fin, we've been down here
              for ages. Everyone must be wondering
              where we are.

Narrator With new hope, the team struggle
              on through the tunnel.

James   What are you guys looking forward to
most when we get out of here?

Leo   Getting my ankle fixed ... fresh air ...
and having something to eat!

Scarlett   I want to see my family again.
My mum and dad will be worried sick.

Alex   Hey, maybe we'll be on the news!

Fin   Yeah, on TV with that woman ...
what's her name? The one
who reads the news!

Narrator   The team's spirits have risen as
the thought of rescue fills their minds.

James   Oh no, my lamp!

Fin   Guys, where are you? Alex, keep still,
you're the only one with a lamp
that works.

Alex   Keep calm, my lamp's fine.
Now keep close and follow me.

Narrator   As it gets darker, the group start
to panic.

James   Oh, Leo, I can't carry you
for much longer.

Leo   Let's stop, my ankle is killing me.

Fin   My arm hurts like mad and it's
bleeding again.

Scarlett   Wait, look! What was that
in the shadows? Alex, shine the lamp
over there.

Alex   It's a man on the ground ... it's Dave!
We're back where we started!

Buried Alive!

Scene 4

PITCH BLACK

Narrator   The team collapse on the ground next to Dave.

Fin   That's it, we've had it now. What a way to die!

Leo   Hey, we're not done for yet. There might be a rescue party looking for us.

Scarlett   What about Dave? Is he still alive?

Alex   What can we do for him?

James   I got my first-aid badge before I got
kicked out of the Scouts.
Let me take a look.

Narrator   James tends to Dave's cut as best
he can. Dave is still knocked out,
but he is alive – just.

Leo   Good work, James! That looks
much better.

Alex   One day we'll look back on this
and tell people how we worked as
a team. How we all pulled together
to get through it.

James   Yeah, to get Leo out, we all
pulled together with our jumpers!

Fin   My arm is really killing me. I'm tired.
I want to go to sleep.

Scarlett   No Fin, try and stay awake.

James   We mustn't give up.
I know, let's sing a song!

Narrator The team tries to keep their spirits up by singing and telling jokes.

James Hold on, guys. There's something we haven't tried yet.

Scarlett What?

James Digging under the rocks!

Narrator James, Scarlett and Alex struggle to move the rocks that are blocking the way out. Leo and Fin are too hurt to help, but they hold the lamp that works.

Scarlett My fingers! These rocks are too heavy!

Alex   We have to try to make a small hole.
Come on, keep digging.

James   It's difficult to see.
Point the light over here more.

Leo   Okay, is that any better?

Fin   Wait, look up there! There's a small
gap at the top of the rock pile!

Narrator Leo points the light to the top
of the rock pile. Sure enough,
there is a small gap at the top.

James   It's too small for me and Scarlett
to fit through.

Scarlett Alex, you're the only one
who can get through there.

Leo   Go for it Alex, it's our last chance!

Fin   You've get to get through before
the lamp runs out. Hurry!

Alex   Okay, but I don't want to leave you
guys alone in the dark.

Narrator   The team decides that Alex must take
the lamp. If he can squeeze through
the hole he'll need it to get to
the surface.

Alex   I'll be back, I promise!

James Quick, just go.

Leo   He's gone. It's so dark ...
Fin? Scarlett? James?

Fin   I'm here Leo, I won't leave you.

Scarlett   I can't see my hand in front
of my face. It's pitch black.

Narrator The team huddles together
next to Dave. They can't see a thing
and the darkness is scaring them.
They can each hear the others sniffing
and trying not to cry.

James How long has Alex been gone?

Fin I don't know. It feels like hours.

Leo Time passes slowly in the dark.
I'm scared.

Scarlett We're all scared, Leo.
We just have to hope.

Narrator Three hours pass and the team
has fallen asleep. Each of them
dreams of sunlight and fresh air.
Suddenly there is a
digging sound ... then CRASH!

James   What the ... Mum, Dad ...
          where am I? Huh?

Alex   Wake up guys, I'm back!
          With a rescue team!

Scarlett   Alex! You dude!

Leo   Am I dreaming? Hold on,
          have you got any food?

Fin   He's real alright, Leo, and so is that
          chocolate bar he's holding!

Narrator   Light fills the cave as the rescue team
          arrives. Dave is carried away safely
          on a stretcher, along with Leo.
          The rest of them follow their rescuers
          to the surface.

Leo What a sight. Those fields and trees
look amazing. Ouch!
Don't bump the stretcher!

Fin I never thought I would see sunlight
again. Wow!

James Well done to Alex. He saved our lives.
Hold on, where is Alex?

Scarlett Look everyone, Alex is over there.
He's talking to that woman
with a microphone.

Fin Hey, is it that woman off the news?

James You know what? I think it is!

Alex Guys, come over here.
They all want to know about how
we were ...

Everyone BURIED ALIVE!

Scene 4   Pitch black

IN THE CHATROOM ...

After the children are rescued from the caves, they write about the experience online.

GREAT ESCAPES — Real-life Stories

Message board: ***Buried Alive!***

Monday 11.05 a.m.
If it hadn't been for me then I don't think we would have made it. I had a lot of good ideas. I made a rope to rescue my mate and I started digging our way out ... The others helped too, though.

Monday 1.30 p.m.
We all worked together to get out of there alive. It was so scary ... especially when we had to cross deep water. A good friend really helped me through that.

- Can you tell which message was posted by which character?

- How can you tell?

TEXTING EMERGENCY ...

Imagine that you're trapped underground like the characters in the play. Your mobile phone has a weak signal – just enough to send a short text message.

- Write a short text message to your parents asking them to send help.
- You can only write up to 15 words.
- Think about the key information you need to tell them. Pick each word carefully.

Tip: Think about what your parents will need to know so they can send help, e.g. where you are. For ideas, find the part in Scene 3 where James calls 999.

ROLE PLAY ...

- *Create a new scene in which the characters tell their story on television news.*
- *In your group, each person chooses a character from the play.*
- *The narrator can be the news reporter asking the questions.*

Tip: Look back through the play for ideas. What key events happened to your character? What is their personality like? Tell the story from your character's point of view.

ASTRO-MAN

TOFFEE NOSE

BURIED ALIVE!

FOUL PLAY

PLANE CRAZY

YARD

DUMPED!

STEP WARS

Interact plays are available from booksellers or
www.risingstars-uk.com

For more information please call 0800 091 1602